Drawings from The National Gallery of Ireland

A Loan Exhibition

Drawings from The National Gallery of Ireland

in aid of The Florentine Art Treasures Fund
(National Gallery of Ireland Appeal)

31 May–7 July 1967

Wildenstein 147 New Bond Street London W1

FOREWORD

Although the paintings in the National Gallery of Ireland enjoy an international reputation, it is not always realized that the Gallery also houses a large group of drawings, watercolours and pastels. In all this numbers about 2,500 items. A large proportion of this collection consists of watercolours made by artists working on both sides of the Irish Sea, not that their inspiration was necessarily derived from their own landscape. We find J. R. Cozens depicting the Bay of Naples or Nathaniel Hone the Younger working in Holland.

In addition, there is a group of Old Master drawings. Some of these, of course, are known to specialists, but others are less familiar. These include a splendid series of drawings by Watteau, of which all but two come from the celebrated collection formed by Miss James in the nineteenth century.

It is one of the aims of this exhibition, which has been selected and catalogued by Denys Sutton, to give some idea of the scope of the collection. We like to think that the general public as well as the specialist will derive pleasure from the exhibition. The historian, naturally, will be fascinated by those drawings which illuminate the creative processes and provide evidence of the artist's approach to composition and design. Others will respond to the sensuousness of line for its own sake and delight in the way that a painter, such as Degas, manipulates pastel, using the texture to secure his special effects.

We are grateful to Mr Sutton, not only for the obvious affection which he has shown for the works when making his choice, but also for his sympathy in wishing to represent Irish art so favourably. Were it not that he recognizes certain values peculiar to Ireland, some of our native artists might hardly have been considered worthy of inclusion in such exalted company.

Those not familiar with the National Gallery of Ireland may be interested to know that it has been open as a public gallery since 1864 and from the beginning has shown an interest in this particular field. It was fortunate to receive from William Smith, F.S.A. 130 drawings of quality between 1872 and 1876 mainly by the masters of English watercolour. Some are in this exhibition.

In 1900 the Gallery acquired, by the gift of Henry Vaughan, of London, an invaluable series of thirty-one drawings by J. M. W. Turner, R.A. In general, however, the best of our Continental works were purchased by former Directors and in particular by George F. Mulvany who between 1864 and 1869 greatly enriched our holding.

We have recently acquired a group of drawings which were originally recorded in the Royal Dublin Society in 1833 and which were transferred to the National Museum in 1878. When these were graciously passed on to us last year we found amongst them two Watteau landscapes, two Vignons, the excellent Peter de Wint *Still life* and the Natoire, all included here. In 1963 Sir Chester Beatty gave us a magnificent gift which included such outstanding works as Cézanne's *Montagne Sainte Victoire*, the Picasso, the Segonzac and the Repin.

We hope of course to continue to add important drawings to the collection and when we open our new extension to the Gallery in Dublin in 1968 we intend to have a special room for drawings with a lighting system which will ensure that each work will be cut off from light rays, except at the time the viewer is studying it.

We would particularly thank Mr Daniel Wildenstein for showing this exhibition in aid of the Florentine Art Treasures Fund and we are proud to share with all who have helped to present the exhibition, and with the art lovers in London, in making some small contribution towards the necessary work of restoration in that great Italian city.

JAMES WHITE,
Director, National Gallery of Ireland.

CATALOGUE

NOTE

The compilation of this catalogue would have been impossible without the information so generously provided by many scholars in this country and abroad. The credit for discoveries should be given to them, not to the *compère*.

Special thanks are due to Philip Pouncey for his assistance in respect of the Italian drawings and to Basil Taylor who helped me with the British Drawings.

I had the good fortune to go through the drawings with Denis Mahon and to benefit from his advice and enthusiasm. James White, Michael Wynne and Miss Hilary Pyle made my work easy; and Jammet's, alas soon to disappear, provided vital encouragement!

I would also like to thank Miss Caroline Bush at Wildenstein's for her help. The number referred to under each entry is that of the National Gallery of Ireland's permanent Catalogue which is now in preparation.

D. S.

FRANCESCO DI STEFANO, known as PESELLINO
*c.*1422–1457, Attributed to

I   LIFE-SIZE HEAD; PROFILE OF A YOUNG MAN

On the verso part of a foot and part of a column in chalk. (Not reproduced.)

Inscribed on verso in an old hand (according to Berenson, it is contemporary) *Ano del Pollaiuolo.*

Black chalk on paper, 39·1 × 24·7 cm. (at widest point).

Number 2233.

Collections   Jonathan Richardson, Snr. (Lugt 2184); Rev. Dr H. Wellesley, his sale, Sotheby's, 25th June 1866, 5th day, Lot 906, £10 10*s.* bought by Mulvany for the Gallery.

Literature   A. E. Popham, *Vasari Society*, 2nd Series, xiii, No. 1 (as Antonio Pollaiuolo); B. Berenson, *Drawings of the Florentine Painters*, 1938 (1951ᵉ) (as Piero Pollaiuolo), Fig. 92.

Exhibited   'Centenary Exhibition', National Gallery of Ireland, 1964 (191).

Philip Pouncey has proposed that this fine drawing might be given to Pesellino, an attribution which has been adopted on this occasion.

ANDREA MANTEGNA 1431–1506, Attributed to

2 PORTRAIT OF FRANCESCO GONZAGA, MARQUESS OF MANTUA
Black chalk with slight wash, on paper, 34·8 × 23·8 cm.
Number 2019

Collections Richard Cosway (Lugt 628); R. Houlditch (Lugt 2214);
Rev. Dr H. Wellesley, his sale, Sotheby's, 25th June 1866.
10th day (as Leonardo da Vinci, 'Portrait of Ludovico Sforza',
Lot 1800) £54, bought by Mulvany for the Gallery.

Literature James Byam Shaw, *Old Master Drawings*, VIII, March, 1928,
pp. 50–54, Pl.56; F. Heinemann, *Giovanni Bellini e I Belliani*,
(n.d.), S.247, p. 126; V. Grashtchenkov in *Essays in the History
of Russian and Western Art*, 1960, pp. 253–293.

Exhibited 'Centenary Exhibition', National Gallery of Ireland, 1964 (193).

The sitter, formerly said to be Lodovico Sforza, called il Moro,
has been identified as Franceso Gonzaga, Marquess of Mantua.
J. Byam Shaw (*op. cit.*), pointed out the resemblance of the
portrait to the bust of Francesco in the Ducal Palace, Mantua and
noted its relationship to Sperandio's portrait medal of him.

The drawing has once, fancifully, been given to Leonardo da Vinci
and was later attributed to Francesco Bonsignori (*c*.1453–1519).
J. Byam Shaw suggested that it was done by Giovanni Bellini,
'*pittore del Domino*', when Francesco was in Venice in 1495 and
when he received his formal appointment as general of the forces
of the North Italian Confederacy against Charles VIII of France.
F. Heinemann disputes the identification with Francesco Gonzaga
(without supplying evidence for his opinion) and has given the
drawing, which he describes as a fragment, to the painter of
A Man in Black in the National Gallery, London (2095);
this he attributes to Marco Marziale (*c*.1440–after 1507). The
attribution to Bellini has also been contested by Grashtchenkov
(*op. cit.*)

Philip Pouncey has suggested an attribution to Andrea Mantegna
and connected Number 2019 with the *Portrait of a Beardless Man*
at Christ Church, Oxford; see E. Tietze-Conrat, *Mantegna*, 1955,
p. 207, Fig.65.

ANDREA MANTEGNA 1431–1506, Workshop of

3 THE CORSELET BEARERS
Pen and sepia on paper, 26 × 26·2 cm.
Number 2187.

Collections Lord Spencer (Lugt 1530); William Esdaile (Lugt 2617);
Rev. Dr H. Wellesley; his sale, Sotheby's, 25th June 1866,
5th day, Lot 884, £17, bought by Mulvany for the Gallery.

An old copy, with a number of variants after Mantegna's *Triumph
of Julius Caesar* at Hampton Court, possibly by a member of the
artist's workshop. It is worth noting that more attention is paid
to the antique details in this drawing than in the original, where
Mantegna stressed his independence of classical models. For a
convenient reproduction of the original see E. Tietze-Conrat,
Mantegna, 1955, Fig. 113.

LORENZO DI CREDI 1459(?)–1537

4 STUDY OF A GIRL'S HEAD
Silverpoint, slightly heightened with thin body colour on paper,
23 cm. in diameter
Number 2069

Collections Rev. Dr Wellesley, his sale, Sotheby's, 25th June 1866, 2nd day,
Lot 363, £8 8s. 0d. bought by Mulvany for the Gallery.

Literature J. Byam Shaw, *Old Master Drawings*, IX, June 1928, p. 6,
Pl. 8; A. E. Popham, *Italian Drawings exhibited at the Royal
Academy*, 1930 (59), Pl. L; B. Berenson, *Drawings of the Florentine
Painters*, 1938, (672a), reproduced.

Exhibited 'Exhibition of Italian Art', Royal Academy, London, 1930 (432);
'Centenary Exhibition', National Gallery of Ireland, 1964 (195).

J. Byam Shaw suggests that the pensive, melancholy mood and
refinement shown in this drawing are paralleled in the *Virgin
Suckling a Child* in the National Gallery, London (593).

ALBRECHT DÜRER 1471–1528

5 SAINT CATHERINE

Inscribed with Dürer's initials but not in his hand.

Pen and sepia on paper, 23 × 14 cm.

Number 2336

Collections Basan; Messrs Colnaghi, from whom purchased in 1898.

Literature 'Notes and Sketches by Albrecht Dürer' selected and edited by Campbell Dodgson, *Dürer Society*, Part 12, 1911, p.7 and reproduced; Campbell Dodgson, 'Some Notes on Dürer'. *The Burlington Magazine*, 20, 1911, p.90 ff., Pl.1a; F. Winkler, *Die Zeichnungen Albrecht Dürer*, II, 1937, (510), and reproduction; Hans Tietze and Erica Tietze-Conrat, *Kritisches Verzeichnis der Werke Albrecht Dürers*, II, 1938, (A 298), p. 108 and reproduced p. 243.

Exhibited '*Meister um Albrecht Dürer*', Germanisches Nationalmuseum, Nuremburg 1961, (202) and also (403); 'Centenary Exhibition National Gallery, Dublin, 1964 (194).

Engraved by Dufresne in *Receuil . . . de la collection du Sr. Basin père*, 1792, Pl. 32.

This important and much discussed drawing represents the figure of Saint Catherine in the triptych commissioned by Martin Tucher for the Church of Saint Sebald, Nuremburg, in memory of Lorenz Tucher, and executed by Hans von Kulmbach (*c*.1480–*c*.1522) in 1513. This picture, which is reproduced in colour in the catalogue of the '*Meister um Albrecht Dürer*' exhibition (*op. cit.*, p.105), was once described by Winkler as the most Italianate painting in German art of Dürer's period.

Opinions are relatively evenly divided amongst experts as to whether this drawing is by Dürer or by Hans von Kulmbach; it should be noted that, until exhibited at Nuremburg in 1961, most, if not all, authorities had pronounced on it without having actually seen it.

Differences occur between the drawing and the finished painting and it may well be that Winkler was right in suggesting that it is by Dürer as well as the two drawings in Berlin and the Albertina, Vienna respectively. However, the catalogue of the Nuremburg exhibition favours an attribution to Hans von Kulmbach.

ALBRECHT DÜRER 1471–1528, After

6 A HARE
Inscribed bottom left: *Albrecht Dürer In Nürmb[er]g*
Pen and wash in bistre, 20·2 × 14·1 cm.
Number 2095

Collection Rev. Dr H. Wellesley, his sale, Sotheby's, 25th June 1866,
3rd day, Lot 511, 11 gns, bought by Mulvany for the
Gallery.

This is a good mid-sixteenth century copy after Dürer's
well-known drawing of a Hare (25·1 × 22·6 cm., signed and dated
1502), in the Albertina, Vienna. See F. Winkler, *Die Zeichnungen
Albrecht Dürer*, 1936, I (248), and reproduced, p.171,
who lists the various copies after the Vienna drawing. It is
interesting to recall that one belonged to the well-known sculptor
Pietro Tacca in 1631.

FRA BARTOLOMMEO 1475–1517

7 HEAD OF A FRIAR
Black chalk on paper, 28·5 × 21·7 cm.
Number 2444

Collection Messrs Colnaghi, from whom purchased, 1902.
Literature B. Berenson, *Drawings of the Florentine Painters*, 1938 (221A).
Exhibited 'Centenary Exhibition', National Gallery of Ireland, 1964 (192).

Berenson (*op. cit.*) noted 'not quite satisfactory, but may be his'.
There seems no valid reason to doubt the attribution.

DOMENICO CAMPAGNOLA 1484–1550, Attributed to

8 LANDSCAPE WITH MARY MAGDALEN PRAYING
Pen and sepia on paper, 33·5 × 19·2 cm.
Number 2038

Collections Richard Cosway (Lugt 628); R. Houlditch (Lugt 2214);
Rev. Dr H. Wellesley, his sale, Sotheby's, 25th June 1866,
11th day, Lot 1940, £10 10s., bought by Mulvany for the Gallery.

Formerly ascribed to Titian. The present attribution is due to
Michael Wynne of the National Gallery of Ireland.

ANDREA DEL SARTO 1487–1531, After

9 VISIT OF THE BLESSED VIRGIN TO ST ELIZABETH
Pen and wash, 22·3 × 28·7 cm.
Number 2272

Collections Sir Thomas Lawrence (Lugt 2445); Sir Frederick Burton, by
whom presented, 1866.
Literature John Shearman, *Andrea del Sarto*, 2 Vols., 1965, II, Sc. 14 iii c
p. 305 (as a copy).

A sixteenth-century copy after the well-known fresco of 1524 in
the Chiostro dell Scalzo, Florence. A small autograph panel
(67 × 89 cm.) is in the Galleria Spada, Rome (Shearman, *op. cit.*,
(71), Pl. 131b).

GIROLAMO FRANCESCO MARIA MAZZOLA
called **IL PARMIGIANINO** 1503–1540

10 CUPID FONDLING AN EAGLE
Red chalk on paper, 17·6 × 14·8 cm.
Number 2064

Collections Benjamin West (Lugt 419); Jonathan Richardson Senr.
(Lugt 2183); Rev. Dr H. Wellesley; his sale Sotheby's 25th June
1866, 2nd day, Lot 355, £2 16s., bought by Mulvany for the
Gallery.

Formerly given to Correggio (c.1494–1534). Philip Pouncey has
pointed out that this is a copy by the youthful Parmigianino of
part of the decorations by Correggio in the cupola of San
Giovanni Evangelista, Parma.

FRANCESCO PRIMATICCIO 1504–1570

11 STUDIES OF DRAPERY
Signed bottom right with the initials *F.P.*
Red and white chalk on paper, 19·7 × 15·5 cm.
Number 2239

Collections Count Moriz von Fries (Lugt 2903); Sir Thomas Lawrence
(Lugt 2445); Sir Frederick Burton, by whom presented, 1866.

The attribution of this drawing to Primaticcio has been endorsed
by Mme Sylvie Béguin of the Louvre.

JACOPO DA PONTE called BASSANO 1515/16–1592

12 STUDY OF A FIGURE AND HANDS
Red and black chalk, heightened with white, on paper,
41 × 27·4 cm.
Number 2323

Collection Desprey and Gutekunst, from whom purchased, 1892.

Formerly attributed to Zurbáran (1598–1664).

BERNARDINO LANINO c.1511–1581/2

13 THE MADONNA AND CHILD WITH ATTENDANT MUSIC-MAKING ANGELS
Pen and bistre, heightened with white on paper, pricked for
transfer, 78·5 × 55·2 cm.
Number 2104

Collection Rev. Dr H. Wellesley, his sale, Sotheby's, 25th June 1866,
14th day, Lot 2412, £12 0s., bought by Mulvany for the Gallery.

Literature J. Byam Shaw, *Old Master Drawings*, X, September 1928,
pp.24–27, Pl.23.

Exhibited 'Centenary Exhibition', National Gallery of Ireland, 1964 (196).

Formerly attributed to Gaudenzio Ferrari (c.1470–1576). J. Byam
Shaw was the first to give this drawing to Lanino, suggesting that
it dates from the time when he was working as an assistant to
Gaudenzio Ferrari at Vercelli or Saranno between 1530 and
1536.

FEDERIGO BAROCCIO 1528–1612

14 STUDY OF A MAN'S HEAD
On the verso is a Study of a Child. (reproduced Fig. 14A).
Pastel on paper, 30 × 20 cm.
Number 2008

Collection Hodder M. Westropp by whom presented, 1864.

GIROLAMO MUZIANO 1528–1592

15 STUDY OF A MALE FIGURE
Carries top left stamp of Royal Dublin Society.
Red chalk on paper, 38·3 × 20 cm.
Number 3840

Collections Royal Dublin Society; transferred to the National Museum, 1879;
transferred to the Gallery, 1966.

Formerly ascribed to Sir Anthony Van Dyck (1599–1641). The
attribution of this powerful drawing is due to Philip Pouncey.

GIOVANNI BATTISTA NALDINI 1537–1591

16 A PIETÀ
Red chalk and sepia, 26·3 × 31·2 cm.
Number 2119

Collections Sir J. C. Robinson (Lugt 1433); F. Muller, Amsterdam, from
whom purchased in 1896.

This connected with the *Pietà* in the Ospizio degli Innocenti,
Florence (Alinari photograph No. 29385), formerly given to
Rosso Fiorentino (1494–1540). There is another similar *Pietà* in
S. Simone, Florence. See Paolo Barocchi, '*Itinerario di Giovambattista
Baldini*' in *Arte Antica et Moderna*, 31–32, 1965, Fig.96a.

FRANCO-ITALIAN c.1550

17 DESIGN FOR THE PROSCENIUM ARCH OF A COURT THEATRE
Inscribed on bottom right, *optimo cniq operconda virtutis in
steumsutury* (?), on bottom left, *Ed Hardman Assist Secretary R.D.S.
103–84.*
Pen and sepia and wash on paper, 50·8 × 28·8 cm.
Number 3841

Collections Royal Dublin Society; transferred to National Museum 1878;
transferred to Gallery, 1966.

Formerly attributed to Francesco Primaticcio (1504–1570).

LEANDRO BASSANO 1557–1622

18   PORTRAIT OF AN ELDERLY MAN
Red and black chalk, 28 × 17·4 cm.
Number 2715

Collection   Francis Wellesley; his sale, Sotheby's, 28th June 1920 ff., 1st day, Lot 672, where purchased for the Gallery.

Formerly given to Annibale Caracci (1560–1609). A drawing of the same sitter was in the Phillippe Fenwick Collection, Cheltenham; see Hans Tietze and E. Tietze-Conrat, *The Drawings of the Venetian Painters*, 1944, Pl. CXLIX, 3.

The Fenwick drawing (now in the British Museum, 1946–7–13–23) has an inscription by Jonathan Richardson, Junior, discussing the identity of the sitter – Paolo Paruta (d.1596). It is also inscribed with an old (but not autograph) inscription, *Carletto*. The Tietzes note that this artist was greatly influenced by Jacopo Bassano in his early days.

GASPARO VERONENSIS (fl.1550), attributed to

19   A PROCURATOR PRESENTED TO ST MARK BY ST VINCENT FERRER
Inscribed with Motto of the family *Semper Idem*.
Tempera on vellum 21·5 × 33 cm.
Number 2328

Collection   Duke of Somerset, Christie's, 28th June 1890, Lot 1, (as a Venetian illumination) 15 gns, bought by Doyle for the Gallery.

According to Sir K. T. Parker, the coat of arms is that of Molin, one of the great Venetian families which produced a seventeenth-century Doge.

Sir K. T. Parker has pointed out that this splendid illumination might well be from the official document confirming the appointment of a Procurator in his office. He has also suggested that the artist might well be Gasparo Veronensis. There is a comparable miniature signed by this artist in a Dogale delivered by Doge Francesco Donato to Marino Venier, captain of Sacile on 5th March, 1551 in the Pierpont Morgan Library, New York (M. 353).

SIR PETER PAUL RUBENS 1577–1640

20   A DRAGON'S HEAD
Pencil and chalk on paper, 17·5 × 20·6 cm.
Number 2606

Collection   Sir Thomas Lawrence (Lugt 2445); purchased 1907.

This drawing, which seems to be autograph, is connected with the large *Fall of the damned* of 1618–20 (*Rubens, Klassiker der Kunst*, 194) in the Munich Gallery.

ADAM ELSHEIMER 1578–1610

21   WOODED LANDSCAPE AT DUSK
Gouache on paper, 16 × 17 cm.
Number 2101

Collections   William Esdaile (Lugt 2617); Rev. Dr Henry Wellesley; his sale, Sotheby's, 25th June 1866, 3rd day, Lot 526, £7 10s., bought by Mulvany for the Gallery.

Literature   Hans Möhle, '*Eine bisher unbekannte Landschaftsgouache von Adam Elsheimer*' in *Zeitschrift des Deutschen Vereins für Kunstwissenschaft*, XIX, (34), 1965, p.192, Pl.11; Hans Möhle, *Die Zeichnungen Adam Elsheimer*, 1966, p.161, (64).

Exhibited   'Centenary Exhibition', National Gallery of Ireland, 1964 (198); '*Deutsche Maler und Zeichner des 17 Jahrhunderts*', Schloss Charlottenberg, Berlin, 1966 (134); '*Adam Elsheimer*', Städelesches Kunstinstitut, Frankfurt-am-Main, 1966–67 (162, Fig.131).

Hans Möhle points out that the compositional arrangement has similarities with that in the gouache belonging to Count Antoine Seilern (Möhle No.63). However, whereas this work may be dated to about 1610, Number 2101 is dated by Möhle to about 1605.

There is a note on the back of the drawing by H. Wellesley, stating that 'The effect of night is so true, that on showing it to a celebrated artist, he fell asleep, just like bed time. October 27th 1841.'

GIOVANNI FRANCESCO BARBIERI
called IL GUERCINO 1591–1666

22   THE VIRGIN AND CHILD

Red chalk on beige paper, 20 × 17·18 cm.
Number 2603

Collection   Robert Udney (Lugt 2248); purchased, 1907.

Denis Mahon has pointed out that this is a study for the upper
part of the early altar-piece by Guercino representing *The
'Madonna del Carmine' presenting a scapular to a Carmelite in the
presence of two Franciscans*, which is in the Pinacoteca Civica at
Cento (reproduced in N. Grimaldi, *Guercino*, 1957, Fig.89).
The Madonna, Child, and the principal figure of the Carmelite
below her are reproduced in reverse in an engraving after
Guercino by G. B. Pasqualini dated 1623, and the Saint is there
identified as Saint Albert rather than Saint Simon Stock, who is
the usual recipient of the scapular. Though the date of 1623 on
the engraving provides a *terminus ante quem*, Denis Mahon believes
this important composition to have been painted considerably
earlier, in about 1614–15, and draws attention to other drawings
related to it. One is in the Pierpont Morgan Library, New York
(see catalogue by Felice Stampfle and Jacob Bean of an exhibition
held at the Morgan Library of drawings from New York
collections entitled *The Seventeenth Century in Italy*, 1967,
pp.35–36 (36), reproduced). A second is at Chatsworth (519), of
which a copy is to be found at Christ Church, Oxford (R.12).
Although the Morgan and Chatsworth drawings are originals,
doubt may be felt concerning Windsor (2479), the
arrangement of which corresponds to an engraving by Bartolozzi
(Baudi di Vesme/Calabi No.2115, in reverse in relation to the
Windsor drawing), made after a drawing which belonged to
Zanetti, and which may have been an original. There also exist
late eighteenth-century imitations based on Bartolozzi's engraving
(in the Brera and Castello Sforzesco; Fogg Museum (268) makes
use of one figure only from Bartolozzi).

GIOVANNI FRANCESCO called IL GUERCINO
1591–1666

23 THE VIRGIN WITH SAINT CATHERINE OF ALEXANDRIA AND A
BANNER OF SAINT DOMINIC
On verso two alternative poses for the Saint Catherine in red
chalk. (reproduced Fig. 23A).
Red chalk, 29·8 × 20·2 cm.
Number 2631

Collection   Purchased in 1907.

In the opinion of Denis Mahon, this drawing is an authentic
example from Guercino's late period. He adds the following
comments. The somewhat archaic arrangement, with the Virgin
holding the banner with the image of St Dominic, suggests a
study for an engraving rather than for an altar-piece. But in the
absence of any such engraving it may be noted that Guercino was
paid 500 scudi for an altar-piece for the Cathedral at Bolzano on
7th September 1655. A price of this order suggests a painting
with four large figures, and in fact Malvasia (*Felsina Pittrice*, 1678,
II, p.380) gives the subject as the Virgin, the Magdalen,
St Catherine and St Dominic.

The composition of the present drawing obviously implies an
additional flanking figure on the left, and there are in fact two or
three faint strokes which suggest the location of its head. If the
drawing were connected with the Bolzano painting the missing
figure would represent the Magdalen, since the remaining three
figures recorded by Malvasia are all present. There is no special
reason (other than the requirements of a particular commission)
for portraying St Catherine on the same canvas as St Dominic;
when this is borne in mind, together with the fact that the style
of the drawing would in no way be inconsistent with a dating of
1655, it seems well within the bounds of probability that the
drawing originated as a study for the Bolzano altar-piece.

SEVENTEENTH CENTURY BOLOGNESE SCHOOL

24 APOLLO
Red chalk on paper, 33·4 × 19·5 cm.
Number 2062

Collection   Rev. Dr H. Wellesley, his sale, Sotheby's, 25th June 1866, 2nd day,
Lot 342, £2 13s., bought by Mulvany for the Gallery.

Formerly attributed to Correggio (*c*.1494–1534).

CLAUDE VIGNON 1593–1670

25   PORCIA

Inscribed bottom right *81–84*. Inventory number in pencil.
Red chalk and pencil on paper, 32·1 × 21·4 cm.

Collections   Royal Dublin Society; transferred to the National Museum in 1878; transferred to the Gallery in 1966.
Number 3837

Engraved by Mariette.

This drawing was engraved in the same direction by Mariette for Père Pierre Le Moyne's *La galerie des femmes fortes*, Paris, chez. Ant de Sommaville, 1647. This large folio volume has a frontispiece and twenty engraved portraits after Vignon.

The engraving which corresponds to Number 3837 is inscribed: *Porcie avale les charbons ardens pour aller après son mary et par la hardiesse et la nouveauté de sa mort égale la réputation de Caton et le gloire de Brutus Valerius Max. lib. 4 Cap. 6'*.

Three other drawings for this series are known. *La Monime* in the Cabinet des Dessins of the Louvre, *La Camme* at Rugby School and a *Dame chrétienne et française* which was in London in 1958. See Pierre Rosenberg, 'Some Drawings by Claude Vignon' in *Master Drawings*, IV (3), 1966, pp.289–293, and Pl.23.

Porcia, a firm Republican, was the daughter of Cato Uticensis and wife of Bibulus. She later married Brutus, Caesar's murderer. According to the *Oxford Classical Dictionary*, the best tradition proves that she died before Brutus in 43 B.C., despite the statement in Valerius Maximus, which Vignon used, that she killed herself by swallowing live coals, after the death of her husband.

CLAUDE VIGNON 1593–1670

26   PAULINA

Inscribed bottom right. *81a–84.* Inventory number in pencil.
Red chalk and pencil on paper, 32·2 × 21·4 cm.
Number 3838

Collections   Royal Dublin Society; transferred to National Museum, 1878;
transferred to Gallery in 1966

Engraved by Mariette.

This drawing was engraved in the same direction by Mariette for
Père Pierre Le Moyne's *La galerie des femmes fortes*, Paris, chez
Ant de Sommaville, 1647. This large folio volume has a frontispiece
and twenty engraved portraits after Vignon.

The engraving which corresponds to Number 3838 is inscribed
'*Pauline résolue de mourir avec Sénèque se fait couper les veines et laisse à
la posterité un parfait exemple d'un amour constant et herioque*' *Tacite
Ann. Li. 15.*

For the other known drawings in this series see the Note on
No.25 (3837).

Paulina Pompeia was Seneca's second wife and much younger
than her husband. She did not commit suicide when her husband
took his life after he had been named in the Pisonian conspiracy
of A.D. 65. She would have done so but for the intervention of
Nero.

JACOB JORDAENS 1593–1678

27   THE ADORATION OF THE KINGS

Red and black chalk and watercolour on paper, 34 × 28 cm.
Number 2597

Collections   Sir Thomas Lawrence (Lugt 2445); Thomas Dimsdale (Lugt 2426);
purchased, 1907.

Literature   R. A. D'Hulst, *De Tekeningen van Jacob Jordaens*, 1956, (96),
Michael Jaffé, 'Jordaens Drawings at Antwerp and Rotterdam',
The Burlington Magazine, 108, December 1966, p.627, Fig.39.

Exhibited   'Centenary Exhibition', National Gallery of Ireland 1964, (200);
'*Tekeningen van Jacob Jordaens*', Rubenshuis, Antwerp, 1966, and
Boymans-van Beuningen Museum, Rotterdam, 1967 (74).

This is connected with the high altar-piece in the Church of
St Nicholas at Diksmuide, dated 1644 (and destroyed in the
1914–18 war) for which the composition sketch is in the National
Gallery of Scotland, Edinburgh. There are numerous variations
between Number 2597 and the painting. Professor R. A. d'Hulst
has suggested that the main portion of Number 2597, which is
more finished than the Edinburgh drawing, is contemporaneous
and that it is a trial of the composition in reverse. This opinion
was endorsed by Michael Jaffé, *op. cit.*

JACOB JORDAENS 1593–1678

28   PIETÀ

Inscribed centre lower edge in ink *Jordaens*, and again in a different hand, on *verso*

Pen, coloured wash and body colour on paper, 25 × 23·7 cm.

Number 2445

Collection   Messrs Colnaghi, from whom purchased, 1902.

Literature   Léo van Puyvelde, *Jordaens*, 1953, p.181, note 157; Léo van Puyvelde in catalogue of '*Le Siècle de Rubens*', Musées Royaux des Beaux-Arts, Brussels, 1965 (116, p.109).

Exhibited   'Centenery Exhibition', National Gallery of Ireland, 1964 (201).

This is a *modello* for the *Pietà*, once in the collections of the Duke of Marlborough and Consul Weber and now in the Kunsthalle, Hamburg (No. 383, canvas, 207·5 × 191 cm) datable to about 1650. There is another version of the *Pietà*, of about the same date, in the Rubenshuis, Antwerp (canvas 208 × 156 cm) for which there is a composition drawing, formerly in the collection of Sir Richard Nosworthy, in the Ashmolean Museum, Oxford. A study for the St John, which may have been used, with variants, in the Hamburg picture, is in the Fogg Museum, Cambridge, Mass. Both pictures are reproduced by Professor R. A. D'Hulst in *Master Drawings*, I (3), Autumn, 1963 Fig. 4 and Fig. 6 respectively. Information from Michael Jaffé.

JAN VAN GOYEN 1596–1666

29   A DUTCH WHARF

Pen and wash, 15 × 19·5 cm.

Number 2127

SIR ANTHONY VAN DYCK 1599–1641, attributed to

30   THE DEATH OF ADONIS

Pen and ink on paper, 19·9 × 16·7 cm.

Number 2607

Collections   Sir Joshua Reynolds (Lugt 1794); Lord St Helens; purchased, 1907.

The old attribution has been provisionally retained. Van Dyck painted a number of pictures with this theme; however, Number 2607 does not correspond precisely to any of the oil versions.

ALBERT CUYP 1605–1691

31   Landscape

Black chalk and wash, 18.8 × 30.5 cm.

Number 2070

Collections   Lord Spencer (Lugt 1530); William Esdaile (Lugt 2617); Miss James, her sale, Christie's, 23rd June 1891, 2nd day, Lot 188, 9 gns (together with a Wouvermans *Peasant on Horseback*), bought by Doyle for the Gallery.

REMBRANDT HARMENSZ VAN RYN 1606–1669

32   SKETCH FOR 'SIMEON IN THE TEMPLE'
On verso; a first thought for the same scene in red chalk with
some pen (reproduced Fig. 32A).
Pen and sepia on paper, 17·2 × 15·5 cm.
Number 2245

Collection   Purchased in Amsterdam, 1896

Exhibited   'Centenary Exhibition', National Gallery of Ireland, 1964 (197).

The free sketch technique suggests a date around 1640–41.
Number 2245 may be compared with the *Triumph of Mordecai*
*c.*1640–41, once in the Lubormirski Collection, Wroclaw, Poland.
See Otto Benesch, *The Drawings of Rembrandt*, 6 Vols. 1954–47,
III (487), Fig.609. It does not relate to the two known pictures
of the subject. See A. Bredius, *The Paintings of Rembrandt*, 1937
(543) and (600).

CIRCLE OF REMBRANDT

33   THE ADORATION OF THE KINGS
Pen and wash on paper, 14 × 13 cm.
Number 2018

Formerly attributed to Ferdinand Bol (1611–1681). This drawing
is closest in style to the work of another Rembrandt pupil
Constantijn Renesse (1626–1680) although it is not by this artist.

ISAAC FULLER 1606–1672

34   STUDY OF A FLOATING FIGURE
Inscribed top right: *one of Fullers maid (?) figures in Mag, Coll; ox.*
Red and white chalk on cartridge paper, 26 × 17 cm.
Number 2114

Collection   Purchased in London, 1892.

This drawing is connected with the painting executed by Fuller in
about 1665 for Magdalen College Chapel, Oxford. The east wall,
for which the picture was destined, had been plastered over to
hide iconoclastic damage and it is not known whether the picture
was painted in fresco or on a very large canvas. It represented the
Founder kneeling between two angels at the Last Judgement. The
picture was destroyed in the 1830's when the Gothic niches were
restored but the general appearance is known from an engraving
by M. Burghers in Adison's *Poems on Several Occasions* (1718), and
from a drawing made by G. C. Cooper in 1811.
In *A Register of the Members of St Mary Magdalen College, Oxford*,
edited by W. D. Macray, 1904, IV, there are the following
references:
'1664 . . . Mag Fuller, pictori, pro arrha, 100^{li}' (p.20).

'1667 . . . Fuller the painter recovered from the Colleges
"pro debitus et damnis" £63 10*s.*, and further Law expenses in
the suit amounted to £22 6*s.* 11*d.*'

HERMAN SAFTLEVEN 1609–1685

35   RUINS
Signed on bottom left with initials and inscribed on verso:
Dit op dandersÿde getekent van Herman Saftleven, is buiten Witte Vrouwe
1674, genaempt den groenen boyart.
Watercolour on paper, 19 × 15 cm.
Number 2264

Collection   Unidentifiable Collection mark; purchased in Amsterdam, 1896.

The inscription means that the motif is taken from outside
De Witte Vrouwenpoort in Utrecht. In Utrecht there still exists a
Wittevrouwensingel. The city gate was demolished in the nineteenth
century.

ADRIAEN VAN OSTADE 1610–1685

36   THE VILLAGE DOCTOR
Pen and wash, 21·7 × 28·5
Number 2675

Collection   Mrs Catterson Smith from whom purchased, 1912.

GERBRANDT VAN DEN EECKHOUT 1621–1674

37   PORTRAIT OF A LADY
Signed and dated *G. V. Eeckhout Fec: 1642.*
Black chalk and wash, 22·2 × 19·3 cm.
The top is shaped as a half-hexagon.
Number 2099.

Collection   Purchased in Amsterdam, 1896.

WALLERANT VAILLANT 1623–1677

38   PORTRAIT OF AN OFFICER
Signed and dated lower right *W. Vaillant. fecit 1648*
Number 2435

Collection   Messrs Colnaghi, from whom purchased, 1901.

The former identification of this portrait as being of Marshal
Turenne is incorrect.

JAN WYNANTS 1630/35–1684

39   LANDSCAPE
Signed lower edge left centre with monogram *JW.*
Watercolour on paper, 21·3 × 33 cm.
Number 2320

Collection   Messrs Colnaghi from whom purchased, 1897.

ADAMS FRANS VAN DER MEULEN 1632–1690

40   A MILITARY CAMP WITH A VIEW OF MAËSTRICHT IN THE DISTANCE
Red chalk on paper, 40·2 × 24·8 cm.
Number 2189

Collection   Presented by Henry, Fifth Earl of Portarlington, 1884.

This is a study for the extreme left-hand side of a composition representing *The Siege of Maëstricht*. There are photographs of two almost identical pictures in the Witt Library, London; one version, canvas, 105 × 146 cm. was in the Maugny Sale, Hôtel Drouot, Paris, 26th May 1933 (Lot 41), and the other, 51 × 81 cm incorrectly entitled *The Siege of Tournai*, was in the Fievez Sale, Brussels, 14th May 1928 (Lot 63).

The city of Maëstricht surrendered to Louis XIV by 1st July, 1673. The king was present with his court, including the Queen, and the Marquise de Montespan, who was about to make him a father again. In conducting military operations, the king was advised by Vauban and, as Maurice Ashley points out (*Louis XIV and the greatness of France*, 1946, p.98), 'A young English volunteer officer named John Churchill played a minor part in this success: a figure of ill-omen for Louis's later career.'

WILLEM VAN DE VELDE 1633–1707

41   THE BATTLE OF THE TEXEL, 11 AUGUST 1673
Signed with initials bottom right and dated *1673* top left.
Pen and wash on paper, 29·5 × 46·7 cm.
Number 2340

Collection   Henry, Fifth Earl of Portarlington, by whom presented, 1884.

M. S. Robinson has identified the subject of this drawing. He points out that Cornelis Tromp's ship, the *Gouden Leeuw* is on the left and in the centre the dismasted *Prince Royal*, flagship of Sir Edward Spragge which put up a stout defence before being towed out of action to safety.

This is a sketch coming near to the finished painting, of which two very similar versions exist, one in the Rijksmuseum, Amsterdam and the other in the National Maritime Museum, Greenwich. There is at Greenwich an earlier sketch (1085) for the paintings; it shows Tromp's ship stern view and the sinking Dutch ship on the right bow view.

The artist's letter b and the dotted lines above the stern of the *Royal Prince* signify an area of blue which he wanted to set against the white smoke below it, which is shown in the painting but not in this drawing.

WILLEM VAN DE VELDE 1633–1707

42 AN ACTION IN THE MEDITERRANEAN AGAINST BARBARY PIRATES
Signed bottom left with initials.
Pen and wash on paper, 19 × 34·8 cm.
Number 2345

Collection Henry, Fifth Earl of Portarlington, by whom presented, 1884.

M. S. Robinson has identified the subject of this drawing. He points out that the English flagship is on the left with an Algerine near her sinking. There is an Algerine flagship in the background and an English vice-admiral can be seen in the distance.
This is a sketch for a painting of which there is a version in the National Maritime Museum, Greenwich. In the painting, the Union flag of the English flagship is at the mizzen and not at the main; the Algerine flagship is in the centre background and the English vice-admiral does not appear. An earlier sketch exists (photograph at Greenwich); in the right background of this there appear to be an English vice-admiral and a rear-admiral but no Algerine admiral.

The action has not been identified. Van de Velde was commissioned to paint a number of actions in the Mediterranean, some of which date before 1672, when he came to England. There is a series of them in the Royal Collection. Many of the actions were quite small ones and were not recorded in printed sources, but they can be found in the logs of the ships which were in the Mediterranean protecting the English Levant trade. If the Union flag at the mizzen as shown in the painting and not the flag at the main is correct, the action should be one in which Sir John Harman, Sir Richard Beach or Sir Roger Strickland took part; these three were 'Rear Admiral in the Streights' in 1669, 1670 and 1678 respectively.

CASPAR NETSCHER 1639–1684

43 PORTRAIT OF A YOUNG MAN
Black chalk on paper, 19·8 × 16·2 cm.
Number 2201a

Collection De Vos, Amsterdam: purchased in Amsterdam, 1896.

CASPAR NETSCHER 1639–1684

44 TWO LADIES AND A GENTLEMAN
Pen and sepia, 14·8 × 13·3 cm.
Number 2201 b

Collection De Vos, Amsterdam; purchased in Amsterdam, 1896.

SEVENTEENTH CENTURY FLEMISH SCHOOL

45   LANDSCAPE
Pen and wash on paper, 16 × 21·5 cm.
Number 2261

Collection   Henry, Fifth Earl of Portarlington by whom presented, 1884.

Formerly attributed to Jacob van Ruysdael (1629/30–1682).
This drawing is here provisionally catalogued as seventeenth-
century Flemish school.

GIUSEPPE PASSERI 1654–1714

46   BACCHANALIAN GROUP
Pen and wash heightened with white, 23 × 55·5 cm.
Number 2750

Collection   The Hon. Mrs Phillimore, by whom presented, 1925, through the
Friends of the National Collections of Ireland.

Formerly given to Pietro da Cortona (1596–1669). The present
attribution is due to Philip Pouncey and John Gere.

ROSALBA CARRIERA 1675–1757

47   PORTRAIT OF A GIRL REPRESENTING 'NIGHT'
Pastel, 35 × 28 cm.
Number 3844.

Collection   Milltown Bequest, 1902.

This is one of a group of six pastels by the artist; four represent
'The Four Seasons' and two represent 'Night' and 'Day'.
They were presumably bought by the first Earl of Milltown in
Italy. According to Brinsley Ford, Joseph Leeson (1711–1783),
created first Earl of Milltown in 1763, visited Italy twice. First in
1744–1745, when he sat to Pompeo Batoni (1708–1787) and
ordered several pictures from Joseph Vernet. Second in 1750–51,
when according to John Steegman (*The Burlington Magazine* LXXXVIII,
March, 1946, pp.55–63) he again sat to Batoni. On this occasion he
was accompanied by his son Joseph Leeson (1783–1801). Both father
and son appear in the caricature groups painted by Reynolds in
1751 which are now in the National Gallery of Ireland. A *Portrait
of Mrs Leeson as a Shepherdess* painted by Batoni in 1751 is in the
collection of Denis Mahon.

Mr Ford has no record of either Leeson having visited Venice but,
as he points out, they would obviously have gone there as it was part
of the Grand Tour.

This pastel formerly hung in the Music Room at Russborough,
Co. Wicklow.

ANTOINE WATTEAU 1684–1721

48 RUSTIC BUILDINGS IN A LANDSCAPE
Inscribed bottom left in ink *Vataux* and *no 51 R Dublin Society
Ed Hardman Assis^t Sec^y 1833 88–84* (Inventory number in pencil).
Red chalk on paper, 21 × 26 cm.
Number 3822

Collections Royal Dublin Society; transferred to National Museum in 1878;
transferred to Gallery in 1966.

One of Watteau's copies after sixteenth-century Venetian
masters. According to Mariette (*Abecadario*, I, 1851, p.294),
Crozat owned a large collection of drawings by Campagnola; in
fact, 123 are listed in Mariette's catalogue of the collection.
Mariette pointed out that '*Vateau les copia tous, étant chez
M. Crozat, et il avouait qu'il en avait beaucoup profité.*' Mr Walter C.
Baker, New York, owns both a Campagnola drawing and
Watteau's copy after it. See Claus Virch, *Master Drawings in the
Collection of Walter C. Baker*, 1962, (11 and 72).

Another drawing after a Venetian landscape carrying the same
inscription *Vataux* is in the Art Institute of Chicago, see Hugh
Edwards, 'Two Drawings by Watteau' in *Museum Studies*, Chicago,
Winter, 1966, pp. 9–13, Fig. 2.

ANTOINE WATTEAU 1684–1721

49 CHURCH, FORTRESS AND RUSTIC BUILDINGS IN A LANDSCAPE
Inscribed *Vataux* bottom left in pen and *No.48 R Dublin Society
Ed Hardman Assis^t Sec^y. 1833 89–84* (Inventory Number in pencil).
Red chalk on paper, 21·3 × 25 cm.
Number 3823

Collections Royal Dublin Society; transferred to National Museum in 1878;
transferred to the Gallery in 1966.

ANTOINE WATTEAU 1684–1721

50   A LADY AND TWO GENTLEMEN
Red chalk on paper, 15 × 16·5 cm.
Number 2300

Collection   Miss James, her sale, Christie's, 23rd June 1891, 2nd day,
Lot 346, 18 gns, bought by Doyle for the Gallery.

Literature   K. T. Parker and J. Mathey, *Antoine Watteau: catalogue de son
œuvre dessiné*, 1956, 2 Vols., I, No.51 (reproduction).

Exhibited   'Centenary Exhibition', National Gallery of Ireland, Dublin, 1964
(202).

The man in the centre, engraved by J. Audran (*Figures de
différents caractères*, published by Jean de Jullienne, 1725–28,
No.342), was used for *La Mariée de Village* (E. Dacier and
A. Vuaflart, *Jean de Jullienne et les graveurs de Watteau au XVIII
Siècle*, 3 Vols., III 1921–29, (111)). The figures on the right
and left were used for *La Conversation* in the Heugel Collection
(E. Dacier and A. Vuaflart, *op. cit.*, No.151).

ANTOINE WATTEAU 1684–1721

51   A LADY STANDING WITH HER BACK TURNED
Red chalk on paper and plumbago, 14 × 9·5 cm.
Number 2299

Collection   Miss James, her sale, Christie's, 23rd June 1891, 2nd day, Lot 322,
£23 2s. bought by Doyle for the Gallery.

Literature   Edmond de Goncourt, *Catalogue raisonné de l'œuvre peint, dessiné et
gravé d'Antoine Watteau*, 1875, (684); K. T. Parker and J. Mathey,
Antoine Watteau: Catalogue de son œuvre dessiné, 1956, 2 Vols., II (611)
and reproduction.

Engraved by L. Cars in *Figures de différents caractères*, published by
Jean de Jullienne, 1725–28 (304).

Edmond de Goncourt wrongly considered this drawing as a study
for *Le Bal Champêtre* (E. Dacier and A. Vuaflart, *Jean de Jullienne
et les graveurs de Watteau au XVIII Siècle*, 3 Vols., 1921–29 (311).
A copy of Number 2299 in the same direction as the engraving is
in the Städelsches Kunstinstitut, Frankfurt-am-Main. It is
reproduced in *Stift und Feder*, Pl.6 under the name of Watteau.

ANTOINE WATTEAU 1684–1721

52   HEAD OF AN ABBÉ
Black and red chalk on paper, 15·3 × 13 cm.
Number 2302

Collections   Miss James, her sale, 23rd June 1891, 2nd day, Lot 319,
£6 16s. 6d. bought by Doyle for the Gallery.

Literature   K. T. Parker and J. Mathey, *Antoine Watteau; catalogue de son
oeuvre dessiné*, 1956, 2 Vols., II, (738) and reproduced.

ANTOINE WATTEAU 1684–1721

53   A YOUNG MAN TUNING A VIOLIN
Black and red chalks on paper, 20·5 × 15·2 cm.
Number 2301

Collections   Brisart; Miss James, her sale, Christie's, 23rd June 1891, 2nd day,
Lot 303 14 gns. bought by Doyle for the Gallery.

Literature   William Gibson, *Old Master Drawings*, IX, June 1928, p.8
Pl.12; K. T. Parker and J. Mathey, *Antoine Watteau: Catalogue
de son œuvre dessiné*, 1956, 2 Vols., II, (836) and reproduction.

The drawing was used in the *Concert Champêtre* (E. Dacier and
A. Vuaflart, *Jean de Jullienne et les graveurs de Watteau au XVIII
Siècle*, 3 Vols., 1921–29 (72).

William Gibson (*op. cit.*) noted a resemblance between the young
man and the little boy who appears in *La Danse* (Charlottenburg,
Berlin): see E. Dacier and A. Vuaflart, *op. cit.*, (76), although, as
he observed, the boy in the picture is some years younger.

ISAAC WHOOD 1689–1752

54   PORTRAIT OF DEAN SWIFT
Signed middle of left side *Whood fᵗ 1730*.
Pencil on paper, 37·2 × 26·7 cm.
Number 2614

Collection   Mrs J. Hamilton, from whom purchased, 1907.

This drawing was presumably done in Ireland as Swift made his
last visit to England in 1727.

JEREMIAH DAVISON 1695–1745

55   PORTRAIT OF A LADY
Insert with colour notes. Black chalk on grey paper, 30·3 × 22·8 cm.
Number 2349

Collection   Earl of Warwick (Lugt 2600): purchased, 1902

The 1928 Dublin catalogue notes that it is probably a sketch for a
full-length *Portrait of a lady*, then in the possession of
Mr Stopford-Sackvill, Drayton House, Northants.

ETIENNE JEAURAT 1699–1789

56   L'ACCOUCHÉE
Signed bottom left: *jeaurat f*.
Black and white chalk and pencil on paper, 27·4 × 18·3 cm.
Number 2436

Collection   Messrs Colnaghi from whom purchased, 1901.

Engraved by Lépicié.

The girl is pouring out chocolate.

CHARLES JOSEPH NATOIRE 1700–1777

57   DESIGN FOR A FOUNTAIN
Inscribed: bottom right in ink *C. Natoire*.
Red chalk on paper, 40 × 24.2 cm.
Number 3839

Collections   Royal Dublin Society; transferred to National Museum, 1878; transferred to the National Gallery 1966.

One of a group of seven decorative designs and studies in the Gallery. Possibly an early drawing done by the artist when in Rome in 1722–28.

FRANÇOIS BOUCHER 1703–1770

58   STUDY OF AN INFANT
Black chalk with white and red on beige paper, 17 × 15·7 cm.
No. 2023

Collections   Two unidentifiable collection marks (Lugt 2680, 622); Obach, London, from whom purchased, 1893.

This could be a study after one of the artist's own children done from life, of which examples are in the National Museum, Stockholm.

THOMAS FRYE 1710–1762

59   PORTRAIT OF AN ARTIST
Black and white chalk on blue paper, 42.4 × 30.8 cm.
Number 2634

Collection   Purchased, 1907.

Nothing is known of the early life of this artist who was born in or near Dublin. As a young man he went to London where he soon built up a profitable practice as a portrait painter. In 1744 he piloted a venture in porcelain-making at Bow, taking out a patent with Edward Heyleyn, a merchant, and became manager of the Bow factory. Fifteen years later he went back to painting. He painted portraits in oil, in crayon and also did miniatures; in later years he produced a number of life-size heads in mezzotint. He was a close friend of Sir Joshua Reynolds.

CHARLES GRIGNION 1716–1810

60   STUDY OF A MAN
Black and white chalk on cartridge paper, 31·9 × 16·6 cm.
Number 2117

This is traditionally known as a study of a Greenwich Pensioner.

PAUL SANDBY 1725–1809

61 THE HUNDRED STEPS, SHOWING WINCHESTER TOWER
Watercolour on paper, 38·5 × 60·4 cm.
Number 2577

Collections (?) Sir Joseph Banks; R. A. Sandby Bequest, 1905.

This is closely related to the gouache of the same scene in the
Royal Library at Windsor Castle; see A. P. Oppé, *The Drawings of
Paul and Thomas Sandby in the Collection of H.M. the King at Windsor
Castle*, 1947 (49), Pl.36. A label on the back of Number 2577
states that it is 'a very early drawing of about 1752, formerly in the
collection of Sir Joseph Banks'. However, the style would suggest
a later date.

THOMAS GAINSBOROUGH 1727–1799

62 LANDSCAPE WITH CATTLE
Chalk, ink and wash on cartridge paper, 27·6 × 36·2 cm.
Number 2115

Collection (?) J. H. Hawkins, by whom presented, 1872.

Literature Walter Armstrong, *Gainsborough and his place in English Art*, 1898,
p.167 (reproduction): Mary Woodall, *Gainsborough's Landscape
drawings*, 1939, p.64 and p.139 (434), Pl.213.

Exhibited 'Bicentenary Exhibition', National Gallery of Ireland, 1927 (2115);
'Gainsborough Drawings', Arts Council, London, 1960–61 (36).

Dr Woodall dates this drawing to about 1777 and places it with
the sketches made for *The Watering Place*, *c*.1777 in the National
Gallery, London. What is probably a sketch for Number 2115 was
in the Thomas Lowinsky Collection: Woodall, *op. cit.* (213).

JAMES BARRY, R.A. 1741–1806

63 PROMETHEUS
Signed bottom right *Barry J. Wⁱ*.
Pen and wash on paper, 27 × 17·6 cm.
Number 2629

Collection Purchased, 1907.

James White points out that this drawing presages an engraving
by Barry of *Venus rising from the sea*.

JURRIAAN ANDRIESSEN 1742–1819

64 VISITORS IN A STUDIO
Black chalk heightened with white on grey cartridge paper,
21 × 26 cm.
Number 2003

Collection Purchased in Amsterdam, 1896.

FRANCIS WHEATLEY, R.A. 1747–1801

65   ENTRY OF THE SPEAKER INTO THE IRISH HOUSE OF COMMONS, 1782
Signed and dated, bottom right: *F Wheatley, del 1782:*
Watercolour on paper, 49·7 × 63·8 cm.
Number 2930

Collection   Purchased, 1932.

The Irish Parliament buildings (now the Bank of Ireland), were designed by one of Dublin's most distinguished architects, Sir Edward Lovett Pearce (*c.*1699–1733), friend and correspondent of Alessandro Galilei. Although a cousin of Vanbrugh and most probably apprenticed to him, Pearce's greatest architectural qualities derive from his study of Palladio during a tour of Northern Italy. Pearce owned a copy of the 1601 edition of the *Quattro Libri*, which he annotated abundantly during his travels and which is now preserved in the library of the Royal Institute of British Architects. He returned to London from his Grand Tour in 1724, to Dublin in 1726. From 1727 he was engaged on designing the new Parliament buildings. The foundation stone was laid on 3rd February 1728 and the first sitting in the New House of Commons was held on 5th October 1731.

The Speaker at the time was Edmond Sexton Pery, who was born in Limerick in 1719. The family originally came from Lower Brittany. Pery was called to the Irish Bar in 1745, and he quickly reached a high position in his profession. In 1751 he was elected M.P. for Wicklow. He was first elected Speaker for the Irish House of Commons in March 1771. He was re-elected in 1776, after some opposition, and in 1783; but he resigned the chair in 1785.

In recognition of his services Pery was raised to the peerage by the title of Viscount Pery of Newtown-Pery, in the county of Limerick. He was strongly opposed to the Union, and ultimately voted against it.

GEORGE CHINNERY 1747–1848

66   PORTRAIT OF THE ARTIST
Pencil and sepia on paper, 18·2 × 13·6 cm.
Number 2699

Collection   Major H. W. Hunt from whom purchased, 1914.

This is a squared study, with some variants, for the artist's *Self-portrait* in the National Portrait Gallery, London (779). The *National Portrait Gallery Catalogue* (1949) dates the picture to about 1845.

JOHN ROBERT COZENS 1752–1797

67   IN THE CANTON OF UNTERWALDEN
Watercolour on paper, 37·2 × 53·7 cm.
Number 2067

Collection   William Smith Gift, 1872.

Literature   C. F. Bell and Thomas Girtin, *The Drawings and Sketches of John Robert Cozens; Walpole Society*, XXIII, 1935 (29).

Exhibited   'Art Treasures: Drawings in Watercolour', Manchester, 1857, (51: as 'Pic du Midi'); International Exhibition, London, 1862 (827).

Probably based on one of the sketches drawn by the artist in 1776. Long known as 'Les dents du Midi, Switzerland', the correct identification of the site is due to C. F. Bell and T. Girtin, *op. cit.* One version of this scene is in the Norman D. Lupton Collection (Bell and Girtin, *op. cit.*, p.32).

JOHN ROBERT COZENS 1752–1797

68   THE BAY OF NAPLES FROM CAPODIMONTE, THE CASTLE OF SANT' ELMO ON THE RIGHT, THE BAY ENCLOSED BY THE DISTANT MONTE ATTARI ON THE LEFT
Watercolour on paper, 50 × 71·5 cm.
Number 2068

Collection   William Smith Gift, 1872.

Literature   C. F. Bell & Thomas Girtin, *The Drawings and Sketches of John Robert Cozens, Walpole Society*, XXIII, 1935 (325, ii).

Exhibited   '*Il Paesaggio Napoletano nella pittura straniera*', Palazzo Reale, Naples, 1952 (12).

Another and larger version is in the British Museum. Bell and Girtin, *op. cit.*, (324, i).

JOHN ROBERT COZENS 1752–1797

69   VIEW IN PIEDMONT
Watercolour on paper, 32·8 × 47·3 cm.
Number 2507

Collection   William Smith Bequest, 1877.

This watercolour is not apparently listed in C. F. Bell and Thomas Girtin, *The Drawings and Sketches of John Robert Cozens, The Walpole Society*, XX, 1935.

This watercolour has been included in the exhibition as further study may clear up the question of its attribution. The light effects are most unusual for Cozens and may suggest that this watercolour was in the nature of an experiment.

THOMAS GIRTIN 1775–1802

70 JEDBURGH ABBEY
Signed lower right *Girtin*.
Watercolour on paper, 45·2 × 61·2 cm.
Number 2120

Collection William Smith Gift, 1872.

Literature Randall Davies, *Thomas Girtin's Watercolours*, 1924, Pl.39;
Thomas Girtin and David Loshak, *The Art of Thomas Girtin*, 1954
(253), p.168 (as 1798).

The artist made other views of the same site; see Girtin and
Loshak, *op. cit.*, (36, 167, 187 and 286). Two watercolours,
View of Jedborough Abbey and *View of Jedborough Abbey, Scotland*,
were exhibited at the 29th exhibition of the Royal Academy,
1797 as (466) and (423).

THOMAS GIRTIN 1775–1802

71 RAINBOW ON THE EXE
Signed and dated bottom left *Girtin 1800*.
Watercolour on paper, 36·2 × 53·2 cm.
Number 2122

Collection William Smith Bequest, 1877.

Literature Randall Davies, *Thomas Girtin's Watercolours*, 1924, Pl.80;
Thomas Girtin and David Loshak, *The Art of Thomas Girtin*, 1954
(345, ii).

Girtin and Loshak, *op. cit.*, p.181 say 'A poor and somewhat
careless replica, harder in colour' than (345, i), then in
the collection of Mr Gilbert Davis and now in the Huntington
Library and Art Gallery, San Marino, California.

JOHN CONSTABLE 1775–1837

72   FLATFORD, DEDHAM VALE
Inscribed bottom left: *Flatford Octr 5 1827* and with colour notes.
Pencil on paper, 22·1 × 32·9 cm.
Number 2057

Collection   Purchased at Christie's, 1892.

This was drawn by the artist when he visited Flatford Mill,
Suffolk, with his children John and Maria for about two weeks in
October 1827. Graham Reynolds has pointed out that it comes
from a sketch-book of which a number of leaves are in the
Victoria and Albert Museum, London. (See *Catalogue of the
Constable Collection*, 1960 (290–300), pp.177–180.)

On the right of the drawing are Flatford Old Bridge and Bridge
Cottage, which are best known as features in the *View on the Stour
near Dedham* exhibited at the Royal Academy in 1822 and now
in the Huntington Library and Art Gallery, San Marino,
California. On the left of the drawing is part of the nearby lock.
The leaves (297, 298, 300) and presumably (293) in the
Victoria and Albert Museum are close at hand, or of the same
scene shown from slightly different viewpoints. Two sheets from
the same sketch-book are in the British Museum and a wash
pencil drawing is, or was in the possession of Mrs E. O. Beazley.

JOSEPH MALLORD WILLIAM TURNER, R.A.
1775–1851

73   THE REICHENBACH FALLS
Watercolour on paper, 47·3 × 31·2 cm.
Number 2431

Collection   Henry Vaughan Bequest, 1900.

This is one of a group of thirty-one drawings by Turner which
was bequeathed to the Gallery by Henry Vaughan on his death
in 1900. A number of these once belonged to the dealer, Thomas
Griffiths.

This watercolour must derive from Turner's first visit to the
Continent in 1802, when he is known to have visited the
Reichenbach Falls. See A. J. Finberg, *A Complete Inventory of the
Turner Bequest*, 2 Vols., 1909, Sketchbooks LXXXIV (69), LXXVII (27)
and LXXV (13), and A. J. Finberg, *Life of J. M. W. Turner, R.A.*, 1961,
p.84 f.

JOSEPH MALLORD WILLIAM TURNER, R.A.
1775–1851

74 PETWORTH PARK
Bodycolour on paper, 13·9 × 19·3 cm.
Number 2430

Collection Henry Vaughan Bequest, 1900.

This dates from the early 1830's. It may be compared with the watercolours in the Turner Bequest, cf. A. J. Finberg, *A Complete Inventory of the Turner Bequest*, 2 Vols., 1909, Sketchbook ccxliv.

JOSEPH MALLORD WILLIAM TURNER, R.A.
1775–1851

75 YARMOUTH
Watercolour on paper, 24·8 × 36·5 cm.
Number 2425

Collection Henry Vaughan Bequest, 1900.

Exhibited Winter Exhibition, Royal Academy, 1892 (68).

Turner visited Yarmouth on various occasions. There are three watercolours of Yarmouth in the Turner Bequest. Number 2425 probably dates from about 1830.

JOSEPH MALLORD WILLIAM TURNER, R.A.
1775–1851

76 THE STELVIO PASS
Watercolour on paper, 24·2 × 30·5 cm.
Number 2419

Collection Henry Vaughan, 1900.

Stelvio Pass (Giogio di Stelvio), is on the Italian-Swiss frontier between the Adda and the Adige.

This was possibly executed by Turner on his journeys of 1835 or 1836. There is a pencil drawing of the pass by the artist in the Turner Bequest, British Museum. See A. J. Finberg, *A Complete Inventory of the Turner Bequest*, 2 Vols., 1909, Sketchbook cccxli.

JOSEPH MALLORD WILLIAM TURNER, R.A.
1775–1851

77 TÊTE NOIRE
Watercolour on paper, 25·6 × 28·3 cm.
Number 2421

Collection Henry Vaughan Bequest, 1900.

Exhibited 'Genève et Mont Blanc', Musée d'Art de Histoire, Geneva, 1965 (102).

This watercolour possibly dates from about 1835–40. There is apparently no other treatment of the subject in the Turner Bequest in the British Museum or at least identified as such.

JOSEPH MALLORD WILLIAM TURNER, R.A.
1775–1851

78   THE GRAND CANAL, VENICE
Watercolour on paper, 21·8 × 31·9 cm.
Number 2426

Collection   Henry Vaughan Bequest, 1900.

Literature   Sir Walter Armstrong, *Turner*, 1902, p.123 (reproduced);
A. J. Finberg, *In Venice with Turner*, 1930, p.160.

Exhibited   Royal Academy (Winter Exhibition), 1892 (66);
'Centenary Exhibition', National Gallery of Ireland, 1964 (204).

Finberg (*op. cit.*) dates this to about 1835.

JOSEPH MALLORD WILLIAM TURNER, R.A.
1775–1851

79   THE DOGE'S PALACE, VENICE
Watercolour on paper, 24 × 30·4 cm.
Number 2423

Collection   Henry Vaughan Bequest, 1900.

Literature   A. J. Finberg, *In Venice with Turner*, 1930, p.161.

Finberg (*op. cit.*) dates this to about 1840.

JOSEPH MALLORD WILLIAM TURNER, R.A.
1775–1851

80   SAN GIORGIO MAGGIORE, VENICE
Watercolour on paper, 22·5 × 29 cm.
Number 2417

Collection   Henry Vaughan Bequest, 1900.

Literature   A. J. Finberg, *In Venice with Turner*, 1930, p.161.

Exhibited   'Centenary Exhibition', National Gallery of Ireland, 1964 (203).

Finberg (*op. cit.*) dates this to about 1840.

PETER DE WINT 1784–1849

81   A GIPSY ENCAMPMENT
Watercolour on paper, 36·6 × 34 cm.
Number 2078

Collection   William Smith Gift, 1872.

PETER DE WINT 1784–1849

82   STILL LIFE
Inscribed bottom right *677–83*, Inventory number.
Watercolour on paper, 29·2 × 26·2 cm.
Number 3866

Collection   Transferred from the National Museum, 1966.

EDWARD HAYES, R.H.A. 1797–1864

83   PORTRAIT OF THOMAS MOORE
Signed and dated bottom right: *By Edw.ᵈ Hayes 1815*
Pencil on paper, 44·3 × 33·7 cm.
Number 2713

Collection   R. Langton Douglas from whom purchased, 1919.

Edward Hayes was born in Co. Tipperary and studied drawing under J. S. Alpenny and at the Dublin Society School. After practising as a miniature painter in Clonmel, Waterford and Kilkenny, he established himself in Dublin in 1831 and was a constant exhibitor at the Royal Hibernian Academy, showing miniatures and small portraits in pencil and watercolours and occasional landscapes. He was elected A.R.H.A. in 1856 and R.H.A. in 1861. He was buried at Glasnevin. His son was Michael Angelo Hayes (1820–1877).

Thomas Moore (1779–1852), became the national lyricist of Ireland by the publication of his *Irish Melodies* (1807–34). His *Lalla Rookh* (1817) won him a European reputation. He was a close friend of Byron whose life he wrote in 1830.

SIR FREDERICK BURTON, R.H.A. 1816–1900

84   SKETCH FOR A PORTRAIT OF A CONNEMARA PEASANT GIRL
Watercolour on paper, 25·8 × 19·6 cm.
Number 3842

Collection   Miss Annie Callwell Bequest, 1904.

Sir Frederick William Burton frequently exhibited at the Royal Hibernian Academy or at the Royal Academy. He travelled widely on the continent, especially in Germany. He was director of the National Gallery, London from 1874 to 1894 and some 450 new acquisitions including many important ones, were made during his régime.

DANTE GABRIEL ROSSETTI 1828–1882

85   PORTRAIT OF JANE BURDEN (MRS WILLIAM MORRIS)
Signed and dated top right: *D. G. R. Oxford, 1858.*
Pen and ink, 49·2 × 37·6 cm.
Number 2259

Collection   D. G. Rossetti sale, Christie's, 12th May 1883, Lot 87, purchased for the Gallery.

Literature   Robin Ironside and John Gere, *The Pre-Raphaelites*, 1948, p.33, Pl.36.

Exhibited   'British Portraits', Royal Academy, London, 1956–57 (736).

This is a study connected with the Union frescoes at Oxford, for *Queen Guinevere*. In 1857 Rossetti and other painters then engaged on the Union frescoes, attended a matinée to watch Miss Ruth Herbert act. In the audience they saw Jane Burden. She was asked to pose and this is probably the first drawing that Rossetti made of her.

35

Jane Burden, daughter of the keeper of a livery stable in Holywell, Oxford, married William Morris in 1859. She became a close friend of Rossetti (some argue she was his mistress), and sat to him frequently. The *Catalogue* of the Royal Academy exhibition quotes Graham Robertson's comment on her: 'Her mind was not formed upon the same tragic lines as her face . . . She was Venus Astarte "betwixt the sun and moon a mystery" and there she had to stay.'

LORD LEIGHTON OF STRETTON, P.R.A. 1830–1896

86 STUDIES OF A GIRL
Black and white chalks on brown cartridge paper, 27·8 × 36·5 cm.
Number 2175

Collection Purchased, 1897.

Literature M. H. Spielmann, 'The Royal Academy Exhibition', *Magazine of Art*, January, 1888, reproduction p.240.

Exhibited ? 'Works by the late Lord Leighton of Stretton', Royal Academy, London, 1897 (304).

One of the various studies made by the artist for his *Captive Andromache* of 1888 in the Manchester City Art Gallery. The figure can be seen on the left of the composition. Another drawing from this group is in the Witt Collection, Courtauld Institute of Art, London. Number 3302. The complete drawing is reproduced in the Magazine of Art, p.240.

NATHANIEL HONE THE YOUNGER 1831–1917

87 FISHING BOAT AT SCHEVENINGEN
Watercolour on paper, 12·7 × 17·8 cm.
Number 3500

Collection Mrs Magdalen Hone Bequest, 1919.

Nathaniel Hone came from a family of artists. He spent some seventeen years in Paris and Barbizon, meeting Millet, Corot, Couture, Manet and Théodore Rousseau. He was a close friend of Henri Harpignies. He also visited Italy and other parts of Europe and on returning to Ireland settled in County Dublin, and worked there quietly for the rest of his life. See Thomas Bodkin, *Four Irish Landscape Painters*, 1920.

The National Gallery contains a large collection of his watercolours, as well as oils, from the Mrs Magdalen Hone Bequest, 1919.

JAMES MCNEILL WHISTLER 1834–1903

88 EVENING
Signed with butterfly
Watercolour on paper, 17·6 × 12·7 cm.
Number 2916

Collection Rt Hon. Jonathan Hogg Bequest, 1930.

Exhibited 'Pictures presented to the City of Dublin to form the nucleus of a Gallery of Modern Art', Royal Hibernian Academy, Dublin, 1904–5, (255) (organized by Hugh Lane).

EDGAR DEGAS 1834–1917

89   LES DEUX ARLEQUINS
Signed bottom left *Degas*.
Pastel on paper, 32 × 24 cm.
Number 2741

Collection   Edward Martyn Bequest, 1924.

Literature   Lillian Browse, *Degas Dancers*, 1949, Pl.170; *Apollo*, LXXXIV, October, 1966, Fig.7.

This is one of a series of pastels inspired by a gala performance given at the Paris Opera on the 26th February 1886. For two other pastels: see Browse, *op. cit.* (169 and 171).

Edward Martyn (1859–1923), was one of the most interesting figures of the Irish Revival. He was a passionate Wagnerian, having visited Bayreuth in the 1880's; he wrote about Palestrina in *The Speaker* as early as 1895. He fought hard for the reform of sacred music in Ireland, winning Archbishop Walsh over to his side, and the Palestrina choir, which he financed, had the distinction of numbering John McCormack amongst its pupils. For an account of his life, see Denis Gwynn, *Edward Martyn and the Irish Revival*, 1930.

At the end of January 1886 he went to Paris with George Moore. On 3rd February Moore wrote to his mother that 'I persuaded Edward to buy two pictures' (quoted by Joseph Hone, *The Life of George Moore*, 1936, p.123). It is reasonable to assume that one if not both of these pictures were the two by Degas, Numbers 2741 and 2740. Joseph Hone has pointed out that the hero John Norton in Moore's novel *A Mere Accident* (1887) is based on Martyn; he owned works by 'the four great painters, Manet, Degas, Monet and Renoir'. The collection is described on pp.72–74. (See Ronald Pickvance, 'A newly discovered drawing by Degas of George Moore', *The Burlington Magazine*, CV, June 1963, pp.276–280).

His Bequest to the Gallery included two oils by Monet and Corot and three watercolours by H. B. Brabazon, Count d'Orsay and William Strang.

EDGAR DEGAS 1834–1917

90   DEUX DANSEUSES DANS LA LOGE
Signed top right *Degas*.
Pastel on paper, 48·5 × 64 cm.
Number 2740

Collection   Edward Martyn Bequest, 1924.

Literature   Lillian Browse, *Degas Dancers*, 1949, Pl.184.

Painted in about 1886–88. Miss Browse (*op. cit.*), p.397, notes that the dancer standing on the left bears a resemblance to Mlle Sallé (Browse, *op. cit.*, Pl.184a).

PAUL CEZANNE 1839–1906

91   LA MONTAGNE SAINTE VICTOIRE
Pencil and watercolour on paper, 47·5 × 61·5 cm
Number 3300

Collection   Sir Alfred Chester Beatty by whom presented, 1954.

Exhibited   'Cézanne Exhibition', Wildenstein, London, 1939 (72);
'Cezanne Watercolours', C. E. M. A., London, 1946 (39);
'Centenary Exhibition', National Gallery of Ireland, 1964 (205).

This watercolour of a *motif* which had long fascinated the artist
dates from about 1904 to 1906.

JOHN BUTLER YEATS, R.H.A. 1839–1922

92   PORTRAIT OF JOHN MILLINGTON SYNGE
Signed and inscribed: *JB Yeats 1905 Jan*ᵘ *J M Synge.*
Pencil on paper, 31·6 × 25 cm.
Number 2937

Collection   Lady Gregory; her sale 1932 where purchased for the Gallery.

Exhibited   'W. B. Yeats A Centenary Exhibition', National Gallery of
Ireland, 1965 (110).

A sketch for the oil portrait in the Municipal Gallery,
Dublin (303).

John Millington Synge (1871–1909) lived in Paris from 1895 until
1899 when he met W. B. Yeats. On Yeats's suggestion he went to
the Aran Islands and the stories he heard there suggested the plots
of his first plays such as *The Shadow of the Glen* (produced 1903)
and *Riders to the Sea* (produced 1904). He was one of the three
literary advisers to the Abbey Theatre, Dublin where his most
celebrated play *The Playboy of the Western World* was produced in
1907.

J. B. Yeats studied art at Heatherley's well-known school in
London in 1887 and became a close friend of J. T. Nettleship,
George Wilson and Edwin J. Ellis. The four men called themselves
the Brotherhood and as Joseph Hone says 'They were literary,
believed in the union of all the arts, worshipped at the shrines of
Blake and Rossetti; and nearly all Yeats' early pictures were
poetic and imaginative.' (See memoir to J. B. Yeats's
Letters to his son W. B. Yeats and others 1869–1922, ed. Joseph Hone,
1944, p.29.) Yeats spent the last fifteen years of his life in
New York where he died.

JOHN BUTLER YEATS, R.H.A. 1839–1922

93   PORTRAIT OF SIR HUGH LANE
Signed and dated lower centre *August 1905 J B Yeats.*
Pencil on paper, 17·5 × 12·7 cm
Number 2866

Collection   Misses E. C. and Lily Yeats by whom presented, 1919.

Exhibited   'W. B. Yeats. A Centenary Exhibition', National Gallery of Ireland, 1965 (60).

Sir Hugh Percy Lane (1875–1915) was one of the leading art experts of his generation. He started his own gallery in London in 1898. He came into contact with the leaders of the Irish Renaissance through his aunt Lady Gregory in 1900. In 1901 he commissioned John Butler Yeats to do a series of portraits of Irish literary and artistic personalities. In the autumn of this year, J. B. Yeats and Nathaniel Hone (q.v.), held a joint exhibition in a Dublin studio. In 1908 Lane founded a Gallery of Modern Art in Dublin and presented to it 154 works of art. As is pointed out in the catalogue of the Yeats Centenary Exhibition, National Gallery, 1965, p.41 'When a new building as specified by him was not agreed on, in 1913 he withdrew 39 pictures and gave them to the National Gallery, London. This bequest created the considerable controversy which has recently been resolved on a temporary basis.'

MARIANO FORTUNY Y CARBO 1841–1874

94   COTTAGE, MULES AND FIGURES
Watercolour on paper, 26.5 × 39 cm.
Number 2972

Collection   Miss Kathleen ffrench Bequest, 1939.

ALBERT MOORE 1841–1893

95   STUDY OF A DRAPED FEMALE FIGURE
Black and white chalk on brown paper, 31 × 20 cm.
Number 3843

Collection   Messrs Brown and Phillips from whom purchased, 1904.

The pose is relatively close to that of the figure on the left in *Dreamers*, 1882 in the City Art Gallery, Birmingham. However, the girl in Number 3843 is seated on a bench, not on a chair as in the painting.

ILYA YEFOMOVITCH REPIN 1844–1930

96   THE SINGER
Signed and dated *Ilya Repin 1916* top right and inscribed *Annerova* top left.
Black chalk and wash on brown paper, 73 × 49 cm.
Number 3295

Collection   Sir Alfred Chester Beatty by whom presented, 1956.

The identity of the singer, Annerova, has not yet been established.

JOHN SINGER SARGENT, R.A. 1856–1925

97   SHIPPING, VENICE
Watercolour on paper, 31 × 46 cm.
Number 2752

Collection   Presented by Mrs Ormond and Miss Sargent in memory of their brother in 1925.

WALTER FREDERICK OSBORNE 1859–1903

98   PORTRAIT OF JOHN HUGHES, R.H.A.
Inscribed: *This is my portrait by Walter Osborne. One of the last pictures he painted. Presented by me to Lucy Stoker May 1903 John Hughes.*
Watercolour on beige paper, 60·8 × 46·5 cm.
Number 2668

Collections   John Hughes; Lucy Stoker; Sir Thornely Stoker, Bart.; Bequest, 1912.

Walter Frederick Osborne studied at Antwerp. He worked much in Brittany and in the latter part of his life painted a considerable number of portraits of distinguished Irish men and women.

The marble sculpture of *Orpheus and Eurydice* by John Hughes is now in the Municipal Gallery of Modern Art, Dublin (102).

John Hughes (1864–date of death unknown) was a prolific Irish sculptor who taught in the Metropolitan School of Art. He befriended W. B. Yeats when he was a pupil at that school.

WALTER RICHARD SICKERT 1860–1942

99   STUDY FOR 'SUSPENSE'
Signed bottom left *Sickert*.
Ink on paper, 37 × 23·8 cm.
Number 3285

Collection   Miss Evie Hone Bequest, 1955.

Literature   Lillian Browse, *Sickert*, 1960, p.88.

This squared-up drawing is a study for *Suspense* in the Ulster Museum, Belfast which was exhibited at the London Group show in 1917. The painting is illustrated in Lillian Browse, *Sickert*, 1943, Pl.44.

WILLIAM BUTLER YEATS 1865–1939

100   HEAD OF A YOUNG MAN
Watercolour on paper, 36·5 × 26·5 cm.
Number 3018

Collection   Miss Pamela Hinkson, from whom purchased, 1948.

Exhibited   'W. B. Yeats, A Centenary Exhibition', National Gallery of
Ireland, 1965 (96).

Executed in 1887. Yeats attended the Dublin Metropolitan School
of Art in Kildare Street from May 1884 until July 1885. Among
his fellow students were his two sisters, later to found the Cuala
Industries, George Russell (AE), mystic poet and economist, and
Oliver Sheppard, the sculptor.

Two pastels by Yeats, *Coole House* and *Library, Coole House*, later in
date than Number 3018 are in the collection of Senator
Michael Yeats.

JACK B. YEATS, R.H.A. 1871–1957

101   PORTRAIT OF THE ARTIST
Signed on bottom right with monogram *JBY*.
Pencil on paper, 35·5 × 25·3 cm.
Number 3319

Collection   Victor Waddington by whom presented in 1961.

Exhibited   'W. B. Yeats. A Centenary Exhibition', National Gallery of
Ireland, Dublin, 1965 (60); 'Jack B. Yeats', Art Shop and Boutique,
Derry, 1964; 'Jack Yeats', Arts Council, Belfast, 1964.

This dates from about 1920.

Jack B. Yeats was born at 23 Fitzroy St., London in 1871, son of
the painter, John Butler Yeats (see Nos. 92 and 93). In 1879 he
returned to his homeland and lived with his grandparents at
Drumcliffe, Sligo, where his brother the poet W. B. Yeats is
buried. Five of his paintings were exhibited at the Armory Show,
New York, 1913. Shared an exhibition with William Nicholson in
the National Gallery, London, 1942. Retrospective Exhibition in
Tate Gallery, London, in Leeds, Aberdeen and Edinburgh in
1948. Retrospective exhibitions various U.S. cities, 1951–52.
(By arrangement with the artist he is to be known as Jack B. Yeats
to distinguish him from his father John Butler Yeats.)

SIR WILLIAM ROTHENSTEIN 1872–1945

102   PORTRAIT OF GEORGE MOORE

Signed and dated top right: *Will R 96.*
Chalk on beige paper, 43 × 34 cm.
Number 2968

Collection   Francis Neilson, by whom presented, 1937.

Literature   William Rothenstein, *Men and Memories*, 2 Vols., 1931,
Vol.I, Fig.33.

Exhibited   'Portraits of the 'Nineties. Drawings by Professor William
Rothenstein', Leicester Galleries, London, 1925 (74 as pastel,
1898); 'W. B. Yeats. A Centenary Exhibition', National Gallery of
Ireland, 1965 (112).

Rothenstein in his memoirs (*op. cit.* pp.241–242), says that
Moore wanted him to make a drawing of him for his next book:
'I think I have arranged for Scott (i.e. Walter Scott), to give you
a fiver for the right to reproduce the drawing. In that case you
will, I suppose, give me the drawing; but for some reason
now forgotten, the drawing was not used and remained on
my hands. Moore said of the drawing, rather fatuously – "Now of
whom do you think it reminds me." I could think of no one like
Moore. "Don't you see a likeness to de Goncourt?" he said.
I couldn't conceive of two men more unlike.' This is presumably
Number 2968.

MAX BEERBOHM 1872–1956.

103   W. B. YEATS

Signed upper right *Max* and inscribed *W. B. Yeats* lower left.
Ink and watercolour on paper, 32 × 18·7 cm.
Number 3773

Collection   Presented by the Friends of the National Collections of Ireland,
1959.

Exhibited   'W. B. Yeats. A Centenary Exhibition', National Gallery of
Ireland, 1965 (12).

Max Beerbohm first met Yeats in the winter of 1893 when the
Irish poet's *Land of Heart's Desire* was performed as a 'curtain
raiser' at the Avenue Theatre, London. For Max's unfavourable
comments on Yeats, see Lord David Cecil, *Max*, 1964, p.261.

SIR WILLIAM ORPEN, R.A. R.H.A. 1878–1931

104 STUDY FOR 'A WESTERN WEDDING'
It bears notes and is squared up.
Pencil, chalk and watercolour, 74·5 × 62 cm.
Number 2948

Collection Knoedler & Co., from whom purchased, 1933.

This is an unfinished study for a group on the left-hand side of the painting reproduced in William Orpen, *Stories of Old Ireland and Myself*, 1924, p.88, under the title of 'A Western Wedding'.

PABLO PICASSO 1881–

105 TWO FEMALE FIGURES
Signed and dated top right: *12 13 Avril 1925 Picasso*.
Pencil on paper, 51 × 41 cm.
Number 3271

Collection Sir Alfred Chester Beatty, by whom presented, 1953.

Literature Christian Zervos, *Pablo Picasso*, 1952, V.5 (453 repr.).

The two girls are perhaps dancers.

WYNDHAM LEWIS 1882–1957

106 PORTRAIT OF JAMES JOYCE
Signed, dated and inscribed: *Wyndham Lewis 1921. Drawing of James Joyce*.
Pen and ink on beige paper, 45·6 × 31·6 cm.
Number 3043

Collection Miss Harriet Weaver by whom presented, 1951.

Literature *The Letters of James Joyce*, ed. Richard Ellmann, III, 1966, reproduction facing p.209.

Joyce and Lewis first met in the summer of 1920 or 1921 when Lewis was in Paris with T. S. Eliot. Lewis would frequently see Joyce on his visits to Paris, but after he published his *Time and Western Man* in 1927 with its detailed criticism of *Ulysses*, their relations, though not broken off, were cool. For a summing up of their relationship, see *The Letters of Wyndham Lewis*, ed. W. K. Rose, 1963, p.130.

Lewis made more than one drawing of Joyce. A very similar drawing to Number 3043 is reproduced in W. Lewis, *Thirty Personalities*, published by Desmond Harmsworth, 1932.
In his foreword Lewis referred to 'the hollow hatchet of the face of Mr Joyce'.

Harriet Shaw Weaver was co-editor of *The Egoist*.

ANDRE DUNOYER DE SEGONZAC 1884–

107 LANDSCAPE WITH TREES
Signed on lower right: *A Dunoyer de Segonzac*.
Pen and watercolour, 48 × 62·7 cm.
Number 3273

Collection Sir Alfred Chester Beatty, by whom presented, 1953.

EVIE HONE 1894–1955

108 DESIGN FOR EAST WINDOW, ETON COLLEGE CHAPEL
Gouache on paper, 121 × 87·7 cm.
Number 3302

Collection Mrs Nancy Connell Bequest, 1958.

Literature C. P. Curran, 'Evie Hone: Stained Glass Worker', *Studies*, XLIV (Summer), 1955; *The Times*, 4th August 1952; *The Listener*, 21st August 1952, p.310.

Exhibited 'Irish Exhibition of Living Art', National College of Art, Dublin, 1952 (39c); '*Irische Kunst der Gegenwart*,' Iserlohn, 1955 (5); 'Evie Hone 1894–1955' University College, Dublin, 1958 (45); 'Evie Hone 1894–1955' (Arts Council), Tate Gallery, London (66).

This is the third of three scale drawings. The lower panels illustrate the Last Supper, with the sacrifice of Melchizidec on the left and Abraham and Isaac on the right, the centre portion is the Crucifixion, and the top shows Christian symbols, surmounted by the Holy Ghost.

This window was commissioned in 1949 to replace that destroyed in the bombing of 1941; it was completed in 1952. Before making the cartoons for the Eton window, Evie Hone drew a preliminary sketch and three scale studies.

A preliminary sketch is in an Irish private collection, the first scale study belongs to Mr Michael Scott, Dublin and the second is in the collection at St Mary's College, Emo Park, County Laois. Another preliminary sketch is in the Tate Gallery, London.
(See *Tate Gallery Catalogue*, 1964, T.204, pp 298–299.)

ILLUSTRATIONS

1 Attributed to Pesellino *Profile of a young man*

2 Attributed to Mantegna *Francesco Gonzaga, Marquess of Mantua*

3 Workshop of Mantegna *The corselet bearers*

4 Lorenzo di Credi *Study of a girl's head*

6 After Dürer *A hare*

5 Dürer *Saint Catherine*

7 Fra Bartolommeo *Head of a friar*

8 Attributed to Domenico Campagnola
Landscape with Mary Magdalen praying

9 After Andrea del Sarto *Visit of the Blessed Virgin to Saint Elizabeth*

10 Parmigianino *Cupid fondling an eagle*

11 Primaticcio *Studies of drapery*

12 Jacopo Bassano *Study of figure and hands*

13 Lanino *Madonna and Child with attendant music-making angels*

14 Baroccio *Study of a man's head*

14A Baroccio *Study of a child* (verso)

15 Muziano *Study of a male figure*

16 Naldini *A Pietà*

17 Franco-Italian
Design for a proscenium arch

19 Gasparo Veronensis, attributed to
A Procurator presented to Saint Mark by Saint Vincent Ferrer

18 Leandro Bassano *Portrait of an elderly man*

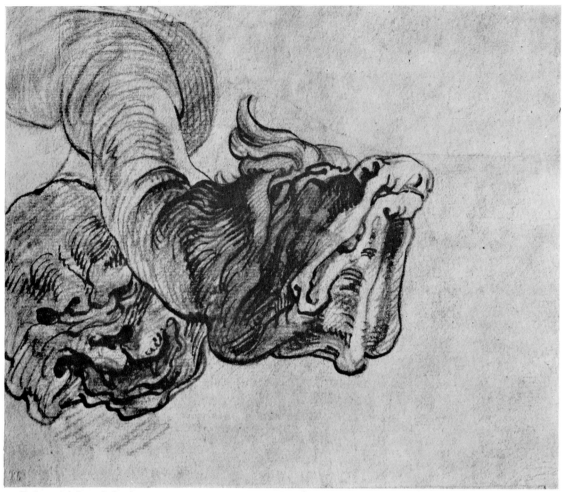

20 Rubens *A dragon's head*

21 Elsheimer *Wooded landscape at dusk*

22 Guercino *The Virgin and Child*

23 Guercino *The Virgin with Saint Catherine of Alexandria and a banner of Saint Dominic*

23A Guercino *Two studies of Saint Catherine of Alexandria* (verso)

24 Seventeenth-century Bolognese School *Apollo*

25 Vignon *Porcia*

26 Vignon *Paulina*

27 Jordaens *The Adoration of the Kings*

28 Jordaens *Pietà*

29 Van Goyen *A Dutch wharf*

30 Van Dyck, attributed to *The death of Adonis*

31 Cuyp *Landscape*

32 Rembrandt *Sketch for Simeon in the Temple*

32A Rembrandt *Sketch* (verso)

33 Circle of Rembrandt *The Adoration of the Kings*

34 Isaac Fuller *Study of a floating figure*

35 Saftleven *Ruins*

36 Van Ostade *The village doctor*

37 Eeckhout *Portrait of a lady*

38 Vaillant *Portrait of an officer*

39 Wynants *Landscape*

40 Van der Meulen *A military camp with a view of Maëstricht in the distance*

41 Van der Velde *The Battle of the Texel, 1673*

42 Van der Velde *An action in the Mediterranean against Barbary pirates*

43 Netscher *Portrait of a young man*

44 Netscher *Two ladies and a gentleman*

45 Seventeenth-century Flemish School *Landscape*

46 Passeri *Bacchanalian group*

47 Carriera *Portrait of a girl representing 'Night'*

48 Watteau *Rustic buildings in a landscape*

49 Watteau *Church, fortress and rustic buildings in a landscape*

50 Watteau *Lady and two gentlemen*

51 Watteau *Lady standing with her back turned*

52 Watteau *Head of an Abbé*

53 Watteau *A young man tuning a violin*

54 Isaac Whood *Portrait of Dean Swift*

55 Davison *Portrait of a lady*

jeaurat f.

56 Jeaurat *L'accouchée*

57 Natoire *Design for a fountain*

58 Boucher *Study of an infant*

59 Frye *Portrait of an artist*

60 Grignion *Study of a man*

61 Sandby *The hundred Steps, showing Winchester Tower*

62 Gainsborough *Landscape with cattle*

63 Barry *Prometheus*

64 Andriessen *Visitors in a studio*

65 Wheatley
*Entry of the Speaker into the Irish House of Commons,
1782*

66 Chinnery *Portrait of the Artist*

67 J. R. Cozens *In the Canton of Unterwalden*

68 J. R. Cozens *The Bay of Naples from Capodimonte*

69 J. R. Cozens *View in Piedmont*

70 Girtin *Jedburgh Abbey*

71 Girtin *Rainbow on the Exe*

72 Constable *Flatford, Dedham Vale*

73 Turner *The Reichenbach Falls*

74 Turner *Petworth Park*

75 Turner *Yarmouth*

76 Turner *Stelvio Pass*

77 Turner *Tête Noire*

78 Turner *The Grand Canal, Venice*

79 Turner *The Doge's Palace, Venice*

80 Turner *San Giorgio Maggiore, Venice*

81 De Wint *A gypsy encampment*

82 De Wint *Still life*

83 Hayes *Portrait of Thomas Moore*

84 Burton *Sketch for a portrait of a Connemara peasant girl*

85 Rossetti *Portrait of Jane Burden (Mrs William Morris)*

86 Lord Leighton *Study of a girl*

87 Nathaniel Hone the Younger *Fishing boat at Scheveningen*

88 Whistler *Evening*

89 Degas *Les deux arlequins*

90 Degas *Deux danseuses dans la loge*

91 Cézanne *La montagne Sainte Victoire*

92 John Butler Yeats *Portrait of John Millington Synge*

93 John Butler Yeats *Portrait of Sir Hugh Lane*

94 Fortuny *Cottage, mules and figures*

95 Moore *Study of a draped female figure*

96 Repin *The singer*

97 Sargent *Shipping, Venice*

98 Osborne *Portrait of John Hughes, R.H.A.*

99 Sickert *Study for 'Suspense'*

100 William Butler Yeats
Head of a young man

101 Jack B. Yeats *Portrait of the Artist*

102 Sir William Rothenstein *Portrait of George Moore*

103 Beerbohm *W. B. Yeats*

104 Orpen *Study for 'A western wedding'*

105 Picasso *Two female figures*

106 Wyndham Lewis *Portrait of James Joyce*

107 Dunoyer de Segonzac *Landscape with trees*

108 Evie Hone *Design for the East Window, Eton College Chapel*